The HomeBuilders

C O U P L E S   S E R I E S

"Unless the Lord builds the house,
they labor in vain who build it."
Psalm 127:1

RESOLVING
CONFLICT
IN MARRIAGE

Study Guide

Bob and Jan Horner

How to Let The Lord Build Your House

and not labor in vain

The Family Ministry is a part of Campus Crusade for Christ International, an evangelical Christian organization founded in 1951 by Bill Bright. The Family Ministry was started in 1976 to help fulfill the Great Commission by strengthening marriages and families and then equipping them to go to the world with the Gospel of Jesus Christ. Our Family Life Conference is held in most major cities throughout the United States and is one of the fastest-growing marriage conferences in America today. Information on all resources offered by the Family Ministry may be obtained by either writing or calling us at the address and telephone number listed below.

■

The HomeBuilders Couples Series: A small-group Bible study dedicated to making your family all that God intended.

Resolving Conflict in Marriage—Study Guide
ISBN 0-8499-8338-X

Unless otherwise indicated, Scripture quotations used are from the New American Standard Bible, copyright 1960, 1962, 1968, 1971 by The Lockman Foundation, used by permission. Scripture quotations marked NIV are from the New International Version of the Bible, copyright 1978 by the New York International Bible Society. Used by permission of Zondervan Bible Publishers.

Dennis Rainey, Director
Family Ministry
P.O. Box 23840
Little Rock, AR 72221-3840
(501) 223-8663

A Ministry of Campus Crusade for Christ International
Bill Bright, Founder and President

CONTENTS

ACKNOWLEDGMENTS

There is a Book which gives hope. It is "profitable for teaching, for reproof, for correction, for training in righteousness; that the man [and woman] of God may be adequate, equipped for every good work" (2 Timothy 3:16–17). Certainly marriage is a "good work." We are grateful to the One who inspired the Bible, and to His Son, for providing the basis for resolving all conflict.

Campus Crusade for Christ has provided the nurturing environment needed for our twenty-three-year marriage. We have been given vision for our lives, time to grow up, training, and the privilege of working among the finest associates possible. You have helped us to know and love the Author of marriage.

The Merediths, founders of the Family Ministry, were the first to give us workable solutions to conflicts we discovered in our marriage. Don and Sally, thank you for the friendship!

Dennis and Barb Rainey are not only the visionaries behind The HomeBuilders Couples Series and thus this study, but are favorite friends and co-workers who have "pushed" us into speaking and writing with the Family Ministry. Thanks for the loving shove, you two!

Ideas and concepts need the shaping of craftsmen. Julie Denker and Dave Boehi, you have chiseled and sanded and polished our work into something to which we are proud to give our signature. We have told you more than once, and we say it again, "You are geniuses!"

To the many groups around the country who first piloted this project . . . thanks for the feedback. Your input was invaluable. You will likely see those contributions as you use this study again.

There really is nothing new under the sun. This study has evolved out of learning from favorite authors such as Paul Tournier, James Dobson, Gary Smalley, H. Norman Wright, Ed Wheat, and Willard F. Harley, Jr., and from some of our favorite people who work alongside us as fellow speakers with the Family Ministry.

How to
Let the Lord
Build Your House

and not labor in vain

FOREWORD

Conflict is a common denominator of every marriage. No relationship is free from the friction caused by our differences and expectations—and by our just being human. Repeatedly this subject is mentioned by our Family Life Conference guests as one of the most critical issues they face in their marriages. Yet few have received the training they need to know how to handle the hurt, misunderstandings, and difficulties encountered in a normal marriage relationship successfully.

That's why I asked Bob and Jan Horner to tackle this thorny problem—to equip you with practical "how-to's" for resolving conflict between husband and wife. For the past twenty-five years, as staff members with Campus Crusade for Christ, the Horners have teamed up to enrich the lives of college students and lay couples all around the world. Since 1982, they have spoken to thousands annually as speakers at our Family Life Conference. And, for the last two years, they've written and fieldtested this material with couples just like you.

You'll find that Bob and Jan have blended together strong biblical principles with practical questions and projects that will challenge you to change the way you think about conflict. The Horners are in touch with the needs of couples and individuals today, and I am confident that their study will encourage you to dig to new and deeper levels of communication as husband and wife.

DENNIS RAINEY
Director of Family Ministry

The HomeBuilders

COUPLES SERIES

"Unless the Lord builds the house,
they labor in vain who build it."
Psalm 127:1

INTRODUCTION

What Is The HomeBuilders Couples Series?

Do you remember the first time you fell in love? That junior high—or elementary school—crush stirred your affections with little or no effort on your part. We use the term "falling in love" to describe the phenomenon of suddenly discovering our emotions have been captured by someone delightful.

Unfortunately, our society tends to make us think that all loving relationships should be equally as effortless. Thus, millions of couples, Christians included, approach their marriages certain that their "love for each other" will carry them through any difficulties. And millions of couples quickly learn that a good marriage does not happen automatically.

Otherwise intelligent people, who would not think of buying a car, investing money, or even going to the grocery store without some initial planning, enter into marriage with no plan of how to make their marriage succeed.

But God has already provided the plan, a set of blueprints for a truly godly marriage. His plan is designed to enable two people to grow together in a mutually satisfying relationship, and then to look beyond their own marriage to others. Ignoring this plan leads to isolation and separation between husband and wife, the pattern so evident in the majority of homes today. Even when great energy is expended, failure to follow God's blueprints results in wasted effort, bitter disappointment—and, in far too many cases, divorce.

In response to this need in marriages today, the Family Ministry of Campus Crusade for Christ is developing a series of small-group Bible studies called The HomeBuilders Couples Series. This series is designed to answer one question for couples:

How Do You Build a Distinctively Christian Marriage?

It is our hope that in answering this question with the biblical blueprints for building a home, we will see the development of growing, thriving marriages filled with the love of Jesus Christ.

The Family Ministry of Campus Crusade for Christ is committed to strengthening your family. We hope The HomeBuilders Couples Series will assist you and your church as it equips couples in building godly homes.

This study, *Resolving Conflict in Marriage*, exists for those who wish to have their conflicts produce greater communication and understanding in their homes. It is composed of six sessions, each built around a concept which will enrich marriages. As you work through the sessions, you will discover vital principles, personally interact with others, and then apply what you have learned to your own marriage.

The Bible: Your Blueprints for a Godly Marriage

> The Bible is alive, it speaks to me;
> it has feet, it runs after me;
> it has hands, it lays hold on me.
>
> Martin Luther

You will notice as you proceed through this study that the Bible is referred to frequently as the final authority on the issues of life and marriage. Although written centuries ago, this Book still speaks clearly and powerfully about conflicts and struggles faced by men and women. The Bible is God's Word and contains His blueprints for building a godly home and for dealing with the practical issues of living.

While Scripture has only one primary interpretation, there may be several appropriate applications. Some of the passages used in this series were not originally written with marriage in mind, but they can be applied practically to the husband-wife relationship.

We encourage you to have a Bible with you for each session. The New American Standard Version, the New International Version, and the New King James Version are three excellent English translations which make the Bible easy to understand.

Ground Rules for These Sessions

These sessions are designed to be enjoyable and informative—and nonthreatening. Three simple ground rules will help ensure that everyone feels comfortable and gets the most out of the study.

1. Share nothing about your marriage which will embarrass your mate.

2. You may "pass" on any question you do not want to answer.

3. Each time between sessions, complete the **HomeBuilders Project** (questions for each couple to discuss and act on). Share one result at the next group meeting.

Resources

The Family Ministry recommends these outstanding aids to maximize your HomeBuilders study experience.

1. If you are doing this as a couple, we would recommend one study guide for each spouse. The leader's guide would also be very beneficial.

2. If you have attended the Family Life Conference, you will find the conference manual to be a useful tool as you go through The HomeBuilders Couples Series.

3. Your best resource is one another—others can help us maximize our lives as we learn to be accountable for our actions and lives. Be accountable to one another and to another couple for the session and projects completion.

The HomeBuilders

COUPLES SERIES

"Unless the Lord builds the house,
they labor in vain who build it."
Psalm 127:1

HOMEBUILDERS PRINCIPLES

HomeBuilders Principle #1: Understanding differences between you and your mate is the first step toward resolving conflict.

HomeBuilders Principle #2: Unresolved conflict creates a potent acid which eats away at a marriage and family.

HomeBuilders Principle #3: A peaceful relationship with your mate is possible when you pursue God's peace in your life.

HomeBuilders Principle #4: Love, commitment, and forgiveness provide the environment for a person to be willing to be known by another.

HomeBuilders Principle #5: To enjoy the privileges of transparency, you need to control the power of the tongue.

HomeBuilders Principle #6: A commitment to becoming a better listener will help you avoid many conflicts and resolve others before they grow too difficult.

HomeBuilders Principle #7: For confrontation to benefit a relationship, truth must be shared with love.

HomeBuilders Principle #8: You must forgive your mate as God has forgiven you.

HomeBuilders Principle #9: The power of forgiveness lies in God's Spirit as He is given control in your heart.

HomeBuilders Principle #10: Forgiving your mate sets you free to experience love and oneness.

HomeBuilders Principle #11: Returning a blessing for an insult helps defeat the cycle of selfishness which can corrode a marriage relationship.

HomeBuilders Principle #12: As you depend on the Holy Spirit for wisdom and power, you will develop the forgiving and gracious heart you need to respond with a blessing rather than an insult.

The HomeBuilders

C O U P L E S   S E R I E S

"Unless the Lord builds the house,
they labor in vain who build it."
Psalm 127:1

A WORD ABOUT
RESOLVING CONFLICT

Conflict is inevitable. The difference between any two couples is not *whether* there is conflict, but *what* the partners do with it when it surfaces. *Resolving Conflict in Marriage* has been prepared for those who wish to have their conflicts produce greater communication and understanding with their mates.

As a couple, you will not be required to relate your personal conflicts within the group. However, you will be encouraged to uncover, discuss, and resolve those conflicts alone as a couple. This study surfaces issues that many couples have carefully suppressed or have purposely ignored. Defusing these "time bombs" is difficult but oh, so necessary; therefore, don't be surprised if it seems you are experiencing *greater* conflict during this study than before you began. It is all part of learning the joy that comes with communication and understanding.

We commend you for investing in your marriage by rolling up your sleeves and digging into what is so important to you and the generations that will follow you—*Resolving Conflict in Marriage.*

BOB AND JAN HORNER

The HomeBuilders

C O U P L E S   S E R I E S

"Unless the Lord builds the house,
they labor in vain who build it."
Psalm 127:1

God's design for marriage
leads to a peaceful relationship
between husband and wife.
Conflict can build this
relationship through communication
and understanding.

1. Introduce yourself to the group by relating the following information:

■ name, occupation, town where you grew up,
■ months/years you dated as a couple,
■ how and where you met.

Use the space below to record your new knowledge of the others in your group.

_____

_____

_____

_____

_____

2. What kinds of conflict do you remember having during your first year of marriage?

_____

_____

3. (Optional) Which of the following animals (or blend of animals) best characterize the way you communicate at home? If you can't find a match, make up your own. (Circle your choice/s.)

- Beagle (friendly and outgoing)
- Porcupine (a little difficult to get close to)
- Turtle Dove (cheery in the mornings)
- Owl (good at evening conversations)
- African Lion (a lot of "roar" around the house)
- Clam (hard to open up)
- Kitten (just give me your lap and I'll purr indefinitely)

Which one would you use to describe your mate?

_____

_____

A. Conflict Is Inevitable

Marriage is an attempt to blend together two distinctly different individuals with differing backgrounds, values, personalities, and male/female distinctives. Conflicts under these conditions are inevitable.

CASE STUDY

They met at the concessions stand at the Frontier Days Rodeo one cool Wyoming evening. They laughed when each of them ordered exactly the same thing—burger without mustard and onions, cherry soft drink, and large fries. They already had at least that much in common.

In fact, they discovered they both loved horses, the mountains, and being away from home. Wyoming seemed to be the right place to connect two people from such opposite parts of the United States. Carrie, now a stockbroker, was raised around horses. Her earliest memories were populated with world-class jumpers. Her bedroom bulletin board was covered with blue ribbons.

Carrie's parents sent her off to college from their home in one of Southern California's most luxurious country-club estates. She originally came to the University of Wyoming to major in business and minor in equestrian science, and after graduation she remained in Wyoming because she loved the area.

When Rick heard the term "country club," he figured it was probably something you carry for self defense when traveling overseas. The small Tennessee mountain farm where he grew up provided only the very basics for life. But from an early age, Rick knew a lot about horses; his dad always managed to have a few around.

Rick had moved to Wyoming five years earlier so he could work on a ranch and see the greatest rodeos in the world. Then he met Carrie, and the idea of staying out West started to look pretty good.

1. As a casual observer, can you see any differences that you think will need attention if Rick and Carrie begin a serious relationship? What are they?

_____

_____

2. What sorts of conflict can you foresee emerging from these differences?

_____

_____

3. Why is it essential for a married couple to learn how to resolve conflict in their relationship?

_____

_____

4. Many other factors can produce conflict in marriage. One is *personality differences* (gregarious vs. solitary, easygoing vs. perfectionistic, emotional vs. reserved, etc.). How can this cause strife?

_____

_____

5. What types of *differing values and philosophies* (about finances, religion, raising children, etc.) produce conflict in marriage? What types of conflicts over these differences have you observed—either in your marriage or in someone else's relationship?

_____

_____

6. How do *differences between men and women* bring about conflict?

_____

_____

7. What is it that women typically don't understand about men?

_____

_____

8. What is it that men typically don't understand about women?

_____

_____

> **HomeBuilders Principle #1: Understanding differences between you and your mate is the first step toward resolving conflict.**

B. The Impact of Conflict

1. Ephesians 4:26 reads, "Be angry, and yet do not sin; do not let the sun go down on your anger."

a. What does "do not let the sun go down on your anger" mean?

_____

_____

b. What does unresolved conflict do to a relationship?

_____

_____

2. How do parents' unresolved conflicts affect children?

_____

_____

3. What did you learn from your parents about handling conflict—good or bad?

_____

_____

> **HomeBuilders Principle #2: Unresolved conflict creates a potent acid which eats away at a marriage and family.**

(to be completed as a couple)

1. Go through the sections we've just completed.

2. What do you think are some common sources of conflict in your relationship?

a. _____

b. _____

c. _____

d. _____

e. _____

3. Conclude your time together by reading the following personal pledge statement:

"I pledge to you that I will use the next six weeks of this HomeBuilders study to build, strengthen, and encourage our marriage. I will make this study a priority in my schedule by faithfully keeping our 'dates,' working through the projects, and participating in the group discussions. You have my word on it."

_____   _____
(signed)   **(date)**

Will you honor your mate by making this pledge your special commitment to him or her for the coming weeks? If so, sign your name in the space provided in *your mate's* study guide to document your commitment.

C. Pursuing Peace

Though conflict is inevitable, it is not God's ideal. God desires that we experience the peace and unity in a married relationship that we long for.

1. Read the following passages:

> Who is the man who desires life, and loves length of days that he may see good? Keep your tongue from evil, and your lips from speaking deceit. Depart from evil, and do good; seek peace, and pursue it. (Psalm 34:12–14)

> So then let us pursue the things which make for peace and the building up of one another. (Romans 14:19)

a. Why do you think God places so much importance on "living in peace"?

_____

_____

b. According to these passages, what are some things that you can do to maintain peace in your marriage?

_____

_____

$2.$ John 14:27 tells us that peace comes from God. Jesus said to His followers on their last evening together, "Peace I leave with you; My peace I give to you; not as the world gives, do I give to you."

a. Based on Jesus' example, what do you think God's peace is like?

_____

_____

b. Why is it futile to try to achieve lasting peace with your mate apart from God?

_____

_____

c. How do you go about finding God's peace in your life?

_____

_____

> **HomeBuilders Principle #3: A peaceful relationship with your mate is possible when you pursue God's peace in your life.**

$3.$ While pursuing peace and resolving conflict in a marriage is important, it needs to be done the right way.

a. How have you seen conflict "resolved" the wrong way?

_____

_____

b. What happens when a person pursues peace on the surface while burying bitterness and resentment?

_____

_____

c. How do people who love a "good, healthy argument" often make the conflict worse?

_____

_____

D. Reflection

1. What is one thing you have learned from this session that you want to apply at home?

_____

_____

2. What do you hope to gain from the rest of this study?

_____

_____

As you can see, the Bible has much to offer to help you work through conflict. In the remaining sessions, you'll learn some practical concepts about transparency, listening, confronting, forgiving, and returning a blessing for an insult.

Each of the six sessions in this study will end with a **Make A Date.** This is the time you set outside each session to do the **HomeBuilders Project.** This will be your only homework. Do not begin working on the next session until you meet together again as a group. Do only the assigned **HomeBuilders Project** between sessions.

Now conclude Session One by setting aside one hour in your schedule to complete **HomeBuilders Project #1.** Your leader will ask you at the next session to share one thing from this experience.

Date	Time	Location

The Secret of Staying in Love by **John Powell**

■ John Powell explains how we can nurture and strengthen loving relationships through the "secret" of staying in love: communication. He details the process of dialogue in simple exercises that give us a new and deeper knowledge of ourselves and those we love.

HomeBuilders Project # 1

Individually: 15 minutes

Write out your answers to the following questions:

1. When you have conflict in your marriage, how does it affect you?

_____

_____

2. If you have children, how does conflict between you and your mate affect them?

_____

_____

3. As you look at how you and your mate relate to each other, how would you rate your effectiveness in handling conflict? Circle the number on the following scale you think most applies to your marriage:

1	2	3	4	5
ineffective				very effective

4. What is one thing you appreciate about how your mate handles conflict in your marriage?

_____

_____

5. Many people withdraw from conflict; others pursue it. Which do you do, and why?

_____

_____

6. If you could change one thing about how you and your mate handle conflict, what it would be?

_____

_____

Interact As a Couple: 30–45 minutes

1. If you didn't have enough time to talk during the **Construction** project, take some more time now. It's important to pinpoint differences which will naturally lead to conflict.

2. Discuss the questions you answered during your individual time.

3. List three things you can start doing now to improve how you handle conflict as a couple.

a. _____

b. _____

c. _____

4.

Commit yourself to put those three ideas into action for at least one week.

Remember to bring your calendar for **Make a Date** to the next session.

Focus

Resolving conflict begins
as we understand
each other through transparency.

1. Begin this session by sharing one thing you learned from **HomeBuilders Project #1.**

2. Read the following quote:

> No one comes to know himself through introspection, or in the solitude of his personal diary. He who would see himself clearly must open up to a confidant freely chosen and worthy of trust.
>
> Dr. Paul Tournier

Most likely your mate knows more about you than anyone else. What is the best part of being known in this way by him/her?

_____

_____

3. What is the worst part about being known in this way by your mate?

_____

_____

A. The Need for Transparency

The word *transparency* is often used to describe two people who are committed to each other, who trust each other and thus are able to know each other well.

Not all people want to be transparent with one another. In fact, many feel that being transparent is one of the greatest risks they can take.

1. As a group, select three words that you think are most descriptive of the word *transparency*. In what ways can these words, applied to two people, help a marriage?

_____   _____

_____   _____

_____   _____

2. Why is it difficult for some people to be transparent with another person?

_____

_____

3. Why is it often harder for men to be transparent than it is for women (especially when it comes to admitting their need for their wives)?

_____

_____

4. Most people marry with the hope of being transparent, of openly sharing their thoughts and feelings with each other. In what ways is this hope of transparency damaged in so many relationships?

_____

_____

5. Why do couples need transparency in marriage?

_____

_____

B. Transparency Demands Openness

Communication takes place in varying degrees of openness. The descriptions and chart that follow help show where transparency fits in the communication continuum. All of these levels of communication are used to some extent in every marriage.

1. LEVEL ONE: Cliché communication allows one to remain safely isolated and alone. It is restricted to greetings and comments which express no opinions, feelings, or real information.

What's an example of cliché communication?

_____

_____

2. LEVEL TWO: Fact communication consists only of the objective discussion of facts. Gossip or data analysis holds others at arm's length.

Share an illustration of how this type of communication occurred in your family this week.

_____

_____

3. LEVEL THREE: Opinion communication involves sharing ideas and opinions. People who communicate on this level open up enough to express what they really think.

4. LEVEL FOUR: Emotional communication involves sharing feelings and emotions leading to complete communication. It involves conveying one's hopes, fears, likes, dislikes, aspirations, disappointments, joys, sorrows, needs, dreams, failures, desires, stresses, sources of fulfillment, discouragements, and burdens.

5. LEVEL FIVE: Transparent communication involves complete emotional and personal truthfulness. Transparency is sharing your heart with another person.

Why is this level of communication one which you should only share with a few people?

_____

_____

(to be completed as a couple)

Individually:

1. Using the information we have just discussed, evaluate how effectively you and your spouse communicate. Using a scale of 1–5, write the appropriate ratings in the chart:

1	2	3	4	5
poor	fair	good	very good	excellent

COMMUNICATION LEVEL	MEANING	RATING (1–5)
LEVEL ONE: Cliché	Nonsharing	_____
LEVEL TWO: Fact	Sharing what you know	_____
LEVEL THREE: Opinion	Sharing what you think	_____
LEVEL FOUR: Emotion	Sharing what you feel	_____
LEVEL FIVE: Transparency	Sharing who you are	_____

2. What is one step you could take to achieve greater transparency?

_____

_____

3. What is one step you think your mate could take to achieve greater transparency?

_____

_____

Interact As a Couple:

Share your conclusions with each other.

C. Four Steps toward Transparency

1. STEP ONE: Begin by being open with God.

a. King David, when trying to rectify relationships, was first transparent with God. Read what he wrote in the Psalms:

> Search me, O God, and know my heart; try me and know my anxious thoughts; and see if there be any hurtful way in me, and lead me in the everlasting way. (Psalm 139: 23–24)

Do you find this type of transparency with God difficult or easy? Why?

_____

_____

b. As you think of being transparent with your mate, why is this first step of utmost importance?

_____

_____

2.

STEP TWO: Commit to create an atmosphere of love, commitment, and forgiveness in your home.

a. Read the following verse: "There is no fear in love; but perfect love casts out fear" (1 John 4:18).

All of us, if we will admit it, have some fears of being known for who we really are. How does fear affect transparency?

_____

_____

How can love "cast out fear"?

_____

_____

b. Read the following passage:

> For this cause a man shall leave his father and his mother, and shall cleave to his wife; and they shall become one flesh. And the man and his wife were both naked and were not ashamed. (Genesis 2:24–25)

The word *cleave* carries the suggestion of total commitment. When the two of you stood before parents, friends, and relatives on your wedding day, you committed to "have and to hold from this day forward . . . ," in spite of the incredible pressures that were sure to come.

How does your total commitment enable your mate to be transparent?

_____

_____

c. Read the following passage:

Let all bitterness and wrath and anger and clamor and slander be put away from you, along with all malice. And be kind to one another, tender-hearted, forgiving each other, just as God in Christ also has forgiven you. (Ephesians 4:31–32)

If you express forgiveness freely and regularly, how does this help your mate be transparent with you?

_____

_____

NOTE: We have only briefly touched on the subject of forgiveness here. Because of its importance in relationships, we have devoted an entire session to it later in the study.

> **HomeBuilders Principle #4: Love, commitment, and forgiveness provide the environment for a person to be willing to be known by another.**

3. STEP THREE: Affirm your mate when he or she practices transparency.

Why is it important for you to affirm and acknowledge your mate's efforts when they occur?

_____

_____

4. STEP FOUR: Pray with one another regularly.

How does praying together openly and honestly promote transparency and intimacy? If you can, share an experience in which this occurred.

_____

_____

D. Stifling Transparency

1. Read through the following case study:

CASE STUDY

Anne is having trouble at her office with Melissa, one of her associates. She confides her frustration to her husband, who replies, "You absolutely must get rid of Melissa. Stand up for yourself, or she will walk right over you! How many times have I told you already: you're too weak, too easy on your people? I wouldn't let her get away with these things. Go and report this to the management!"

a. What has Anne's husband done to stifle her attempt at being transparent with him?

_____

_____

b. To what level of communication (see chart in **Construction** section) will she likely resort during future encounters with him?

_____

_____

c. Read Ephesians 4:29:

Let no unwholesome word proceed from your mouth, but only such a word as is good for edification according to the need of the moment, that it may give grace to those who hear.

Write a more appropriate response that Anne's husband could have given, following the advice in Ephesians 4:29.

_____

_____

2.

Read the following passages from the Book of Proverbs:

When there are many words, transgression is unavoidable, but he who restrains his lips is wise. (Proverbs 10:19)

There is one who speaks rashly like the thrusts of a sword, but the tongue of the wise brings healing. (Proverbs 12:18)

The one who guards his mouth preserves his life; the one who opens wide his lips comes to ruin. (Proverbs 13:3)

a. What counsel do these Proverbs offer to you as you seek to be more transparent with your mate?

_____

_____

b. Some marriage relationships have been damaged when people tell friends about things their mates have shared with them in confidence. How can you maintain your mate's trust?

_____

_____

> **HomeBuilders Principle #5: To enjoy the privileges of transparency, you need to control the power of the tongue.**

E. Reflection

1.

What is one thing you have learned from this session that you want to apply in your life?

_____

_____

Make a date with your mate to meet in the next few days to complete **HomeBuilders Project #2.** Your leader will ask you at the next session to share one thing from this experience.

Date	Time	Location

■

To Understand Each Other   **by Paul Tournier**

■ The ability to understand each other is what counts in working out marital happiness together. With wisdom and warmth, Swiss psychiatrist Paul Tournier suggests ways to achieve this understanding.

HomeBuilders Project #2

Individually: 20 minutes

1. In what ways has the love and understanding provided by your mate helped you be more transparent? Think of some specific instances.

_____

_____

2. Describe a recent situation in which your transparency was stifled either by criticism or by advice from your mate. Tell how that made you feel about being transparent again on that particular subject.

_____

_____

3. Go through the "Four Steps Toward Transparency" in the **Blueprints** section. What practical steps can you take to begin creating an atmosphere in which you are free to be transparent? Write out an action plan.

_____

_____

_____

_____

_____

_____

_____

_____

_____

_____

Interact As a Couple: 25 minutes

1. Read to each other your responses from your individual time in this **HomeBuilders Project.** Allow these to be read without comment.

2. Talk together about your mutual need for understanding in the areas where transparency may be stifled.

3. Discuss your action plans. What specific steps do you need to take to encourage transparency in your marriage?

_____

_____

_____

4. Pray together for sensitivity and loving understanding in future communication times.

Remember to bring your calendar for **Make a Date** to the next session.

Resolution of conflict
requires a commitment to listen.

1. Begin this session by sharing one thing you learned from **HomeBuilders Project #2.**

2. During this session we will talk about listening. What are some ways you can tell if a person is not listening to you when you are talking?

_____

_____

3. Complete this statement: "When another person isn't listening to me, the thing that bothers me most is _____

_____ ."

If we don't hear one another, we can't achieve understanding. And without understanding, it's impossible to resolve conflict. So becoming a good listener is a key step toward resolving conflict and opening the lines of communication.

A. Poor Listening Habits Fuel Conflict

SKIT
THE CONSEQUENCES OF POOR LISTENING

MODERATOR: It has been a long, trying Monday for both Brian and his wife, Linda. Fall is Brian's favorite time of year because of his love for professional football, and Monday night is his favorite night of the week. Linda enjoys an occasional game as well and has joined him in the family room. The end of the day and the smell of hot popcorn promises a pleasant evening at home together—or does it?

LINDA: "Brian, I wonder why our new neighbors always leave their garage door open. Wouldn't you think they would be afraid of someone stealing their things?"

BRIAN: "I don't know."

LINDA: "I was thinking . . . we need to have them over sometime. I wonder if they know anyone around here. Maybe next weekend we could invite them and some of our friends over for a barbecue."

BRIAN: "Uh-huh."

LINDA (sarcastically): "I can tell you are really concerned about these people, Brian."

BRIAN: "Hmmmm."

LINDA: "Your mom called yesterday, honey. She says that all your dad wants for his birthday this year is another TV set—for the bathroom. Can you imagine, Brian, a TV set in the bathroom?"

BRIAN: "What kind does he want?"

LINDA: "You're just like your dad! If you had TV in the bathroom you'd never come out—and you're in there too long as it is."

BRIAN: "Would you mind getting some salt for the popcorn, Linda?"

LINDA (a little heated): "You get your own salt!"

BRIAN: "Now wait a minute! You know I don't want to miss any of this game. Now get the salt!"

LINDA (sarcastically): "I think it would be all right for you to miss just a little of the game. You certainly have missed a lot of this conversation."

BRIAN (with strong emotion): "Look, I'm not in this room to be talking. Do I have to take this TV set into the bathroom to watch this game? Maybe I will go in there—at least I won't be interrupted!"

LINDA (sarcastically): "Fine! Shall I slip the salt under the door, or do you want to come out during a commercial?"

1. What poor listening habits are Brian and Linda exhibiting?

_____

_____

2. How do poor listening habits make an argument worse than it needs to be?

_____

_____

3. If you were Brian, how could you listen to your wife better and still enjoy the evening's game?

_____

_____

4. If you were Linda, what could you have done to get your husband to talk with you more?

_____

_____

5. Can you recall an argument between you and your mate that was aggravated by your poor listening? Share it with the group.

_____

_____

6. Read the following Proverbs:

He who gives an answer before he hears, it is folly and shame to him. (Proverbs 18:13)

A fool finds no pleasure in understanding but delights in airing his own opinions. (Proverbs 18:2, NIV)

What guidance do these verses provide for:

a. Brian and Linda?

_____

_____

b. You?

_____

_____

(to be completed as a couple)

Individually:

1. How would you evaluate yourself as a listener? For each question below, circle the response that is most true of you.*

a. As your mate talks to you, do you find it difficult to keep your mind from wandering to other things?

Yes   No   Sometimes

b. When your mate talks, do you go beyond the facts being discussed and try to sense how he or she is feeling about the matter?

Yes   No   Sometimes

c. Do certain words or phrases your mate uses tend to prejudice you so that you cannot objectively listen to what is being said?

Yes   No   Sometimes

d. When you are puzzled or annoyed by what your mate says, do you try to get the questions straightened out as soon as possible?

Yes   No   Sometimes

* These questions reprinted by permission from H. Norman Wright, *Communication: Key to Your Marriage*, (Ventura, Calif: Regal Books, 1974), 56–57.

e. If you feel it would take a lot of time and effort to understand something, do you go out of your way to avoid hearing about it?

Yes   No   Sometimes

f. When your mate talks to you, do you try to make him or her think you are paying attention when you are not?

Yes   No   Sometimes

g. When you are listening to your mate, are you easily distracted by outside sights and sounds (such as the TV set, someone walking by, music, the kids, etc.)?

Yes   No   Sometimes

2. Now evaluate your mate as a listener. For each of the seven questions listed above, place an "X" over the response most true of him/her.

Interact As a Couple:

Take a few minutes to discuss your answers with each other.

B. Listening Helps Defuse Conflict

1. What did you learn about yourself and your mate during the **Construction** project? How can you use that information to improve your communication?

_____

_____

2. What are some of the benefits of being a good listener? List as many as you can.

_____

_____

_____

_____

3. When your mate really listens to you, how do you feel? In what ways does your mate's listening build you up?

_____

_____

4. Read James 1:19: "Let everyone be quick to hear, slow to speak . . ."

a. What would happen in most of your marital conflicts if you applied this principle?

_____

_____

b. Think of a recent example in which you as a couple applied this truth and were drawn together because of it.

_____

_____

_____

HomeBuilders Principle #6: A commitment to becoming a better listener will help you avoid many conflicts and resolve others before they grow too difficult.

C. Becoming a Good Listener

1. STEP ONE: Maintain a teachable heart.

a. What happens to communication if you are not teachable?

_____

_____

_____

b. Read the following passages:

A wise man will hear and increase in learning. (Proverbs 1:5)

Incline your ear and come to Me. Listen, that you may live. (Isaiah 55:3)

How can listening to God help you become a better listener with your mate?

_____

_____

_____

2. STEP TWO: Give your mate focused attention.

Focused attention involves several elements:

■ Picking the proper time and place.

■ Making sure there are no distractions.

■ Maintaining eye contact.

■ Allowing enough time to work through the conflict.

a. What have you found to be good times and places for talking about important subjects or working through conflict with your mate?

_____

_____

_____

b. What are some poor times and places?

_____

_____

3.

STEP THREE: Commit to understanding your mate.

Good listening requires more than focusing on what the person is saying. Your goal is truly to understand what your mate thinks, wants, and feels.

> Each one speaks primarily in order to set forth his own ideas. Exceedingly few exchanges of viewpoints manifest a real desire to understand the other person.
>
> Dr. Paul Tournier

> You husbands . . . live with your wives in an understanding way. (1 Peter 3:7)

a. What important things do you do to ensure that you understand what your mate is saying?

_____

_____

b. Stop for a couple of minutes and think of a time when God has given you greater understanding about a conflict with your mate because you took the time to listen to him or her. If you can, share about this experience with the group.

D. Reflection

1.

Look back over this session and select the scripture that was most meaningful to you. Why did you choose this passage?

_____

_____

2.

What is one thing you have learned from this session that you want to apply to your life?

_____

_____

Make a date with your mate to meet in the next few days to complete **HomeBuilders Project #3.** Your leader will ask you at the next session to share one thing from this experience.

Date	Time	Location

Recommended Reading

Communication: Key to Your Marriage **by H. Norman Wright**
(chapters 4 and 9)

■ In this book, Dr. Wright's ideas are ready to help you not just talk about communication, but do it effectively. Learn more than a dozen ways to cope with marital conflict, plus ten practical principles for building your partner's self-esteem through understanding and respect, ten methods for handling angry feelings, and ten steps to avoiding the high cost of anxiety and worry.

Achieving the Impossible: Intimate Marriage **by Charles M. Sell**
(chapter 6)

■ In this book, Dr. Sell reveals the principles that will allow you to make individual differences work for your marriage, to face and handle conflicts, to deal with life's inevitable crises, to develop intimacy, and to be a caring listener.

Individually: 10–15 minutes

1. Review the entire **Blueprints** section.

2. What do you think are your mate's strengths and weaknesses when it comes to listening?

_____

_____

3. What are your own strengths and weaknesses when it comes to listening?

_____

_____

4. What are some practical steps you can take to become a better listener?

_____

_____

5. Summarize your desire to become a better listener by writing a brief pledge to your mate, in 50 words or less. Make it from the heart:

Dear _____ :

_____

_____

_____

_____

_____

_____

_____

_____

_____

_____

_____

_____

Love, _____

Interact As a Couple: 30–40 minutes

1. Select an area of current conflict between the two of you (children, stepchildren, finances, a purchase, in-laws, schedule, social event, etc.).

2. HUSBAND: Take 5–10 minutes to give your point of view about the above issue while your wife listens without comment.

WIFE: When your husband is finished, repeat to him what you heard by using one or all of the following phrases:

■ "What I understand you to say is . . ."

■ "Do I understand you to mean . . .?"

■ "You may not have meant this, but what I heard you say is . . ."

Allow him to clear up any misunderstood communication, but at this point, don't make a specific effort to resolve the conflict. Simply allow your mate to speak to a listening ear.

3. Now, switch roles. WIFE: Explain your viewpoint. HUSBAND: Repeat to her what she just said, allowing her, too, to speak to a listening ear.

4. Of what value has this brief exercise in listening been to each of you?

_____

_____

_____

_____

_____

_____

5. Read to each other the pledges you wrote in question #5 of the individual section of this **HomeBuilders Project.** Talk together about how the two of you can build better listening habits.

6. Close your time together in prayer and commit before the Lord to listen to each other better.

Remember to bring your calendar for **Make a Date** to the next session.

The HomeBuilders

C O U P L E S   S E R I E S

"Unless the Lord builds the house,
they labor in vain who build it."
Psalm 127:1

*Loving confrontation
can help a relationship by offering
a way to practice real love.*

1. Begin this session by sharing one thing you learned from **HomeBuilders Project #3**.

2. In any relationship, there are times when you must confront someone about a problem, a misunderstanding, a transgression, or even a bad or annoying habit. What are some good or bad ways of confronting that you have observed—among children, teenagers, parents, adults, etc.?

_____

_____

3. What are some ways people try to avoid confrontation?

_____

_____

A. Choices for Dealing with Conflict

We have begun to learn that conflict can draw two people together by bringing greater understanding, or it can drive a wedge of resentment and fear between them. Most of us tend to avoid conflict because we have not been taught effective ways to face it.

1. There are four possible ways of dealing with conflict:

Fight to Win: The "I win, you lose/I'm right, you're wrong" position. Domination is usually reflected in this style; personal relationships take second place to the need to triumph.

Withdraw: The "I'm uncomfortable, so I'll get out" position. Viewing conflict as a hopeless inevitability kills the interest in even trying to work out a resolution. Personal relationships take second place to avoiding discomfort.

Yield: The "Rather than start another argument, whatever you wish is fine" position. People who take this approach assume it is far better to be nice, to submit, to go along with the other's demands than to risk a confrontation. To them, a safe feeling is more important than a close relationship.

Lovingly Confront: The "I care enough about you to deal with this issue as it really is" position. This approach offers the maximum possibility of satisfactory resolution with the minimum of threat and stress. The relationship is valued as higher than winning or losing, escaping, or feeling comfortable.

2. What is your usual style of handling conflict?

_____

_____

3. Has your style changed since you became a Christian? If so, how?

_____

_____

4. How do you think your style of handling conflict affects your mate?

_____

_____

B. We Can Learn about Conflict from Real People

The Bible is filled with real people—people in conflict. Determine which of the four styles of dealing with conflict are exhibited in each of the following dramas:

1. Adam and Eve were discovered by God after eating the forbidden fruit.

> Then the Lord God called to the man, and said to him, "Where are you?" And he [Adam] said, "I heard the sound of Thee in the garden, and I was afraid because I was naked; so I hid myself."
>
> (Genesis 3:9–10)

a. How did Adam and Eve respond to this conflict with God?

_____

_____

b. What are ways couples withdraw from each other in marriage?

_____

2. Saul discovered that his son, Jonathan, was befriending young David, the object of the king's intense jealousy: "Then Saul hurled his spear at him to strike him down." (1 Samuel 20:33)

a. What was Saul's style of handling conflict?

_____

_____

b. Why is this style so common in marriage? What are some "spears" that husbands and wives typically hurl at each other?

_____

_____

3. Pharaoh's officials spotted Abram and Sarai as they traveled in Egypt. Abram feared for his life, and he also knew that Pharaoh liked beautiful women:

And it came about when he came near to Egypt, that he said to Sarai his wife, "See now, I know that you are a beautiful woman; and it will come about when the Egyptians see you, that they will say, 'This is his wife'; and they will kill me, but they will let you live. Please say that you are my sister so that it may go well with me because of you, and that I may live on account of you."
(Genesis 12:11–13)

a. What was Abram's way of dealing with this conflict?

_____

_____

b. How can yielding in a conflict and not confronting it truthfully make the conflict worse?

_____

_____

4. Both the Old and New Testaments depict examples of yet another style.

a. The would-be executioners of an accused adulteress encircled Jesus and the woman. Jesus said to them: "He who is without sin among you, let him be the first to throw a stone at her." (John 8:7)

What style did Jesus use to deal with this conflict? Can you think of other times when Jesus used this style?

_____

_____

b. Read the following Proverb: "Better is open rebuke than hidden love. Wounds from a friend can be trusted." (Proverbs 27:5–6, NIV)

How can the "open rebuke" of "a friend" be helpful?

_____

_____

(To be completed as a couple)

1. Think of a recent misunderstanding between you and your spouse. (It may have been over finances, children, vacation plans, choices, schedule, relatives, clothing, the car, etc.) How did you each respond? Circle your answer.

HUSBAND	WIFE
Fight to Win	Fight to Win
Withdraw	Withdraw
Yield	Yield
Lovingly Confront	Lovingly Confront

2. How did you feel when your mate used his/her approach to dealing with this conflict?

_____

_____

3. What would you do differently next time?

_____

_____

4. What would you prefer your mate to do differently next time?

_____

_____

C. Steps to Loving Confrontation

The words *loving* and *confrontation* don't appear to be complimentary. One word is "friendly" while the other tends to make you want to fight back. However, the combination of these two words into the phrase "loving confrontation" describes an important approach to resolving conflict. Loving confrontation is the balanced use of truth and love.

1. STEP ONE: Look inward.

Read Galatians 6:1:

> Brethren, even if a man is caught in any trespass, you who are spiritual, restore such a one in a spirit of gentleness; each one looking to yourselves, lest you too be tempted.

a. According to this passage, what three prerequisites should you meet before you correct someone?

_____

_____

b. Why is looking inward before confrontation so important?

_____

_____

2. STEP TWO: Pick the right time and place.

Read Proverbs 25:11: "Like apples of gold in settings of silver is a word spoken in right circumstances."

a. How would you define the "right circumstances" for loving confrontation in your marriage?

_____

_____

b. MEN: What are the typically appropriate and inappropriate times or settings for your wife to bring up a difficult but necessary issue with you?

_____

_____

c. WOMEN: What are the typically appropriate and inappropriate times or settings for your husband to bring up a difficult but necessary issue with you?

_____

_____

3. STEP THREE: Speak the truth in love.

Read the following directive from Ephesians 4:15:

Speaking the truth in love, we are to grow up in all aspects into Him, who is the head, even Christ.

a. What does it mean to speak the truth in love?

_____

_____

b. How have you applied this principle in your marriage?

_____

_____

c. What happens to a relationship when one person speaks truthfully, but without love?

_____

_____

d. What happens to a relationship where there is love without truth?

_____

_____

e. Which is easier for you to share, love or truth? Why?

_____

_____

> **HomeBuilders Principle #7: For confrontation to benefit a relationship, truth must be shared with love.**

f. Even if you choose the right time and setting, you still need to approach the subject with proper focus. Fill in the following blanks, which pinpoint the proper focus for loving confrontation:

INSTEAD OF FOCUSING ON:	FOCUS ON:
many issues	_____
the person	_____
character	_____
generalizations	_____
judgment of actions	_____
past grievances	_____
judgment of motives	_____
who's winning or losing	_____

D. The Wrong Way to Confront: A Case Study

CASE STUDY

"Honey, it seems that every time you are with my relatives you get real quiet. What is it . . . don't you like them? Maybe it's my brother . . . or Mom. . . . You won't even look her in the eye when she talks to you. What's wrong with you? Look at these family pictures at Christmas. I think you are actually refusing to smile. How long has it been since you called my dad and suggested having breakfast with him? You know he'd love it. Why are you doing this?"

1. What mistakes do you see in this attempt at "loving confrontation"?

_____

_____

2. What's a better way to handle this confrontation?

_____

_____

E. Reflection

What one point or idea was most helpful to you in this session? Why?

_____

_____

Make a date with your mate to meet in the next few days to complete **HomeBuilders Project #4.** Your leader will ask you at the next session to share one thing from this experience.

Date	Time	Location

∎

Caring Enough to Confront   **by David Augsburger**

∎ Discussing trust, anger, change, prejudice, blame, guilt, loyalty, and conscience, the author describes a lifestyle for Christians who care enough to risk confronting others when differences become important. An excellent book for Christians who care about relationships—adults, youth, pastors, couples.

Individually: 30 minutes

1. Review the three "Steps to Loving Confrontation" in the **Blueprints** section.

2. In which of these three areas do you personally struggle the most?

Interact As a Couple: 30 minutes

1. Go over your answers to the question you answered individually.

2. Come to a consensus on the best way to handle confrontation in your marriage.

3. One of the biggest mistakes couples make in confrontation is adopting a "you" focus in their confrontations. "You" messages usually come across as attacks or criticisms. They seek to fix blame on the other person. "I" messages are usually much clearer and more honest, and they don't place blame.

Using "I" instead of "you" statements is much less threatening to the person you're confronting. The following exercise will give you practice in recognizing and using "I" language and other ways of focusing confrontation appropriately.

Work together to turn the "you" messages in the following chart into "I" messages. To give you an example, the first two are done for you.

"YOU" MESSAGES	"I" MESSAGES
You don't understand me!	I feel misunderstood!
You don't budget our money!	I'm concerned about our finances. Can you help me?
You are gone too much!	_____
You are always late!	_____
You are blaming everything on me!	_____
You make me angry!	_____
You never tell me you love me!	_____
(Write a few that you tend to use:)	_____
_____	_____
_____	_____
_____	_____
_____	_____

4. As pointed out in the session, loving confrontation often is misfocused. Check the areas in which you most often get out of focus as you confront your spouse:

_____ Raising many issues at once instead of just one issue at a time.

_____ Focusing on the person rather than the problem.

_____ Focusing on my mate's character rather than specific behavior.

_____ Using generalizations rather than specifics.

_____ Judging actions rather than expressing feelings.

_____ Using "You" statements rather than "I" statements.

_____ Judging motives rather than observing facts.

_____ Concentrating on who is winning or losing rather than striving for mutual understanding.

5. Pray together, asking the Lord for His help and wisdom as you deal with conflicts.

Remember to bring your calendar for **Make a Date** to your next session.

(Optional)

HomeBuilders Project #4b

Individually: 30 minutes

1. Write down one concern about which you feel you need to confront your mate.

2. Using the information discussed in the **Blueprints** section and in **HomeBuilders Project #4a,** write out how you will confront your mate on this subject.

3. Review again the information from Session Three on developing proper listening habits.

Interact As a Couple: 30–60 minutes

1. Take turns sharing your concerns with each other. As your mate confronts you, be sure to apply proper listening habits as you seek mutual understanding of the problem.

2. Spend some time in prayer together, asking for His strength to work through you.

Remember to bring your calendar for **Make a Date** to your next session.

The HomeBuilders

C O U P L E S   S E R I E S

"Unless the Lord builds the house,
they labor in vain who build it."
Psalm 127:1

For peace to replace conflict,
both husband and wife
must take responsibility to
forgive each other.

1. Share something you learned from **HomeBuilders Project #4.**

2. Read the following case study:

CASE STUDY

Charlie and Ellen have come to you for counsel. They are Christians, but during your time together they express intense feelings of anger and bitterness toward one another. You know well that there must be a history of selfishness, disappointment, and mistrust between them. You are relieved to hear of their faithfulness to each other but wonder how such resentment has grown over these twelve years of marriage.

"I can never feel any forgiveness toward Charlie anymore," Ellen says, while Charlie retorts, "I'd like to forgive my wife, but I can't change the way I feel. I can't change the past."

a. What do you think might have contributed to this couple's coldness toward each other over the years?

_____

_____

b. What do you think their relationship will be like in another five years?

_____

_____

c. How would you counsel them?

_____

_____

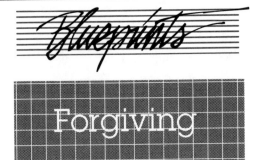

A. What Is Forgiveness?

1. Think back to a time in your life when you received forgiveness from another person for something you did to him or her.

a. Describe the situation.

_____

_____

b. How did you feel before and after you received forgiveness?

_____

_____

2. From that experience, what would you say it means to forgive another person? What is forgiveness?

_____

_____

3. Our Lord provides the best model for what forgiveness is. What do each of the following passages say about God's forgiveness?

God was in Christ reconciling the world to Himself, not counting their trespasses against them. (2 Corinthians 5:19)

_____

_____

There is therefore now no condemnation for those who are in Christ Jesus. (Romans 8:1)

_____

_____

And their sins and their lawless deeds I will remember no more. (Hebrews 10:17)

_____

_____

He made you alive together with Him, having forgiven us all our transgressions. (Colossians 2:13)

_____

_____

Since hurt and disappointment and unmet expectations are inevitable in a marriage relationship, we need to know how to respond when we experience them. Some people don't want to admit their hurt; they withdraw and hide their feelings. Others want to get even by inflicting the same type of hurt. But just as God forgave us of every sin we ever committed against Him, so do we need to forgive our mates. By forgiving your mate, you give up the right to punish him or her. And you decide, as an act of your will, to not hold your mate's mistakes against him or her.

4. Why is the kind of forgiveness described in the previous verses and statement so essential in a marriage relationship?

_____

_____

5. Why do you at times find it difficult to ask your mate for forgiveness?

_____

_____

6. Why do you find it difficult to grant forgiveness when you've been wronged?

_____

_____

HomeBuilders Principle #8: You must forgive your mate as God has forgiven you.

B. How to Ask for Forgiveness

Read the following passage, the well-known story of the prodigal son:

> A certain man had two sons; and the younger of them said to his father, "Father, give me the share of the estate that falls to me." And he divided his wealth between them. And not many days later, the younger son gathered everything together and went on a journey into a distant country, and there he squandered his estate with loose living.

Now when he had spent everything, a severe famine occurred in that country, and he began to be in need. And he went and attached himself to one of the citizens of that country, and he sent him into his fields to feed swine. And he was longing to fill his stomach with the pods that the swine were eating, and no one was giving anything to him. But when he came to his senses, he said, "How many of my father's hired men have more than enough bread, but I am dying here with hunger! I will get up and go to my father, and will say to him, 'Father, I have sinned against heaven, and in your sight; I am no longer worthy to be called your son; make me as one of your hired men.'"

And he got up and came to his father. But while he was still a long way off, his father saw him, and felt compassion for him, and ran and embraced him, and kissed him. And the son said to him, "Father, I have sinned against heaven and in your sight; I am no longer worthy to be called your son."

But the father said to his slaves, "Quickly bring out the best robe and put it on him, and put a ring on his hand and sandals on his feet; and bring the fattened calf, kill it, and let us eat and be merry; for this son of mine was dead, and has come to life again; he was lost, and has been found." (Luke 15:11–24)

This passage illustrates three steps to asking for forgiveness:

1. STEP ONE: Take responsibility for your wrong actions.

a. What indicates that the prodigal son took responsibility?

_____

_____

b. Why is taking responsibility an essential part of asking and receiving forgiveness?

_____

_____

2. STEP TWO: State your error and humbly ask the person to forgive you.

How did the prodigal son accomplish this step?

_____

_____

3. STEP THREE: Take steps to change your behavior and/or make restitution.

a. How did the prodigal son accomplish this step?

_____

_____

b. When a person doesn't try to change the behavior he or she asked forgiveness for, what does this do to the relationship?

_____

_____

c. Share an example of someone who asked for and received your forgiveness for an offense, but never changed his or her behavior. What did this do to the relationship?

_____

_____

d. Share an example—from your marriage, if possible—of a time when you or your mate did change your behavior after receiving forgiveness.

_____

_____

C. How to Grant Forgiveness

Read the following passage:

> This I say therefore . . . that you walk no longer just as the Gentiles also walk, in the futility of their mind. . . . Lay aside the old self . . . be renewed in the spirit of your mind . . . and put on the new self, which in the likeness of God has been created in righteousness and holiness of the truth. . . . Let all bitterness and wrath and anger and clamor and slander be put away from you, along with all malice. And be kind to one another, tender-hearted, *forgiving* each other, just as God in Christ also has forgiven you. (Ephesians 4:17, 22–24, 31–32, emphasis added)

1. STEP ONE: Give up the right to punish your mate.

a. What does Ephesians 4:31 tell us to do with our negative feelings?

_____

_____

2. STEP TWO: Yield to God's command to forgive, in the power of the Holy Spirit.

a. Read the following passages:

> But the fruit of the Spirit is love, joy, peace, patience, kindness, goodness, faithfulness, gentleness, self-control; against such things there is no law. (Galatians 5:22–23)

> And do not get drunk with wine, for that is dissipation, but be filled with the Spirit. (Ephesians 5:18)

Why is it important to be filled with the Holy Spirit as you seek to forgive your mate?

_____

_____

> **HomeBuilders Principle #9: The power of forgiveness lies in God's Spirit as He is given control in your heart.**

b. Why do you think God *commands* us to forgive rather than asking us to forgive when we feel like it?

_____

_____

c. Think of a time when you obeyed God even though you didn't feel like it. How did God bless you as a result?

_____

_____

3. STEP THREE: Don't dwell on the past.

a. How does the Lord regard our past sins for which He has forgiven us?

_____

_____

b. Read Isaiah 43:18–19:

Do not call to mind the former things, or ponder things of the past. Behold, I will do something new, now it will spring forth; will you not be aware of it? I will even make a roadway in the wilderness, rivers in the desert.

How can you apply this passage to the subject of forgiveness?

_____

_____

c. When you choose to forgive your mate in light of God's forgiveness and in obedience to Him, what kind of freedom will you likely experience?

_____

_____

"To forgive is to set a prisoner free . . . and discover that the prisoner was you."

Dr. Lewis Smedes

HomeBuilders Principle #10: Forgiving your mate sets you free to experience love and oneness.

(to be completed as a couple)

Read the following case study and answer the questions together:

CASE STUDY (continued)

Charlie and Ellen are still with you, trading verbal cannonballs.

Ellen: "Charlie makes me feel so unlovable. He always has to be right. The things he has said to me when angered, the way he treats me around the kids, his arrogant ways in front of my parents . . . I just can't let him get by with this. Why should I forgive him? He made his bed, let him sleep in it!"

CHARLIE: "If I've hurt her, then she deserves it. I work hard all day to provide for her needs, and all I hear is griping. I can never do enough, never say things just right; I can never be kind enough to her folks. She's done more than her share to make me miserable. I've only balanced the scales!"

$1.$ What do Charlie and Ellen need to do along with choosing to forgive each other?

_____

_____

_____

_____

$2.$ How should you apply the phrase, "just as God in Christ also has forgiven you," when:

a. You find yourself continuing to think about things your mate has done to you in the past?

_____

_____

_____

_____

b. You want to remind your mate of a way he or she has hurt you in the past?

_____

_____

_____

Make a Date with your mate to meet in the next few days to complete **HomeBuilders Project #5.** Your leader will ask you at the next session to share one thing from this experience.

| _____ | _____ | _____ |
| Date | Time | Location |

Caring Enough to Forgive   by David Augsburger

■ David Augsburger is a forceful writer with a compassionate heart for the needs of people. This book is the second in a new series of "Caring Enough" books.

How Can It Be All Right When Everything Is All Wrong?   by Lewis B. Smedes

■ The experience of "real believing" is the subject of this remarkable book. Author Lewis Smedes shows what it means—and how it feels—to get in touch with "the kind of believing you do with your deepest self, down deep where your primeval feelings flow." *How Can It Be All Right When Everything Is All Wrong?* helps us to grow in awareness of the presence of God inside us. This book doesn't explain away the fact that things get bad. Instead, it helps us move beyond a disheartening present by being open to God and the certainty that things are fundamentally all right.

How to Experience God's Love and Forgiveness   by Bill Bright

■ This booklet is one of ten that give you the "how-to's" of consistent Christian living. All ten are excellent for personal enrichment and as gifts for growing Christians.

Love Life for Every Married Couple   by Ed Wheat

■ In this book, Dr. Wheat explores marital conflict in a straightforward manner, focusing on the reasons why couples experience frustration and unhappiness in their love life.

Individually: 30 minutes

1. Review the session in its entirety.

2. Complete the following two statements, to be shared with your mate:

a. "My greatest difficulty in offering you forgiveness is _____

_____ ."

b. "The one thing that would make it easier for me to ask your

forgiveness is _____ ."

3. Write down some instances in which you have received forgiveness from your wife/husband and have seen healing occur in your relationship as a result.

_____

_____

_____

4. What are some things for which you need to ask your wife's/ husband's forgiveness now?

_____

_____

Interact As a Couple: 30–40 minutes

1. Share your answers to the first three questions you answered individually (questions 1–3).

2. HUSBAND: Ask your wife what you can do to make it easier for her to admit wrong and seek your forgiveness. Record her input below:

_____

_____

_____

_____

3. WIFE: Ask your husband what you can do to make it easier for him to admit wrong and seek your forgiveness. Record his input below:

_____

_____

_____

_____

4. Now it's time to practice what you've been learning. Share your answers to the fourth question you answered individually (question 4).

5. Pray together. Thank God for His unending grace and for His Holy Spirit, who enables you to forgive each other "just as God in Christ has forgiven you."

Remember to bring your calendar for **Make a Date** to your next session.

People have a natural tendency
to respond to hurts with anger.
God promises to help us
exchange these natural reactions
for supernatural responses.

1. Begin this session by sharing one thing you learned from **HomeBuilders Project #5.**

2. In each of the following situations, what would be the normal, natural response?

SITUATION A: Your husband has just embarrassed you at a party by disclosing personal information.

_____

_____

_____

SITUATION B: Your wife is quietly watching television. You slip up behind her in a romantic mood and begin rubbing her neck. She snaps, "Don't you see I'm involved in this program?"

_____

_____

_____

_____

3. What do you think would be the best thing to say to your mate in each situation?

SITUATION A:

_____

_____

_____

_____

SITUATION B:

_____

_____

_____

_____

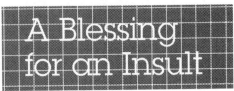

A. Disappointment and Hurt Are Inevitable in Marriage

1. Why is it that the best of friends can sometimes end up bitter enemies?

_____

_____

2. Why are hurt and disappointment inevitable in marriage?

_____

_____

Since hurt and disappointment will occur in your marriage, you need to decide how you want to respond to these painful experiences. You have a choice: you can return an insult with another insult, or you can give a blessing instead.

B. Returning an Insult with an Insult

Read the following scriptural command:

> To sum up, let all be harmonious, sympathetic, brotherly, kindhearted, and humble in spirit; not returning evil for evil, or insult for insult, but giving a blessing instead; for you were called for the

very purpose that you might inherit a blessing. For "let him who means to love life and see good days refrain his tongue from evil and his lips from speaking guile. And let him . . . seek peace and pursue it. For the eyes of the Lord are upon the righteous, and His ears attend to their prayer, but the face of the Lord is against those who do evil." (1 Peter 3:8–12)

1. What does "returning evil for evil, or insult for insult" mean?

_____

_____

The insult-for-insult relationship is defined as "meaning to hurt by remark or action." A person is hurt, so he wants to get even, saying in essence, "What you did hurt me, so I am going to hurt you back." This type of relationship is rooted in an unforgiving and hardened heart attitude. Selfishness is at its core.

2. How do you see children "returning evil for evil, or insult for insult" as they relate to each other?

_____

_____

3. How have you seen this type of response in your own marriage or in others' marriages?

_____

_____

4. What situations or circumstances tend to provoke this type of response in you?

_____

_____

5. What happens to a marriage if it never grows out of the "insult for insult" mode? How have you seen couples unleash the "insult for insult" response on each other during divorce proceedings?

_____

_____

C. The Power of the "Blessing for Insult" Relationship

1. Read 1 Peter 3:8–12 again. What does "giving a blessing" mean?

_____

_____

2. What additional insights do you gain about giving a blessing from the following verses?

> Never pay back evil for evil to anyone. Respect what is right in the sight of all men. (Romans 12:17)

_____

_____

> But I say to you who hear, love your enemies, do good to those who hate you, bless those who curse you, pray for those who mistreat you. (Luke 6:27–28)

_____

_____

The blessing-for-insult relationship can be defined as "continual, active kindness." It is rooted in a forgiving and gracious heart. It means that when your mate disappoints you or hurts you, your responsibility is to find a way to bless him or her. Giving a blessing means that your hope is in God and His Word and that you choose to do good to another regardless of what he or she has done to you.

INSULT-FOR-INSULT RELATIONSHIP	BLESSING-FOR-INSULT RELATIONSHIP
Human perspective	Divine perspective
Based on selfishness and circumstances	Based on God's Word, the unseen
Results: punishment, anger and barriers	Results: purposeful action, transparency
Reactive: emotionally centered; following natural instincts	Responsive: God-centered; supernatural response
Attitude: tear down, depreciate; provoke the other person more	Attitude: build up, appreciate; provoke confession, godliness, and blessing

HomeBuilders Principle #11: Returning a blessing for an insult helps defeat the cycle of selfishness which can corrode a marriage relationship.

3. What are some things you've seen your mate do to give a blessing after an insult?

_____

_____

4. What are some other practical ways you can give a blessing?

_____

_____

_____

D. Three Steps to a "Blessing" Relationship

First Peter 3:8–12 outlines three simple steps leading to blessing relationships.

1. STEP ONE: "refrain your . . . tongue from evil"

Why do you think it is so important to control your tongue?

_____

_____

2. STEP TWO: "turn away from evil and do good"

How do you "turn away from evil"? What kind of impact does this response have on a conflict?

_____

_____

3. STEP THREE: "seek peace and pursue it"

What is one way you can apply this step in your marriage?

_____

_____

(to be completed as a couple)

Individually:

Conflict often grows out of differences in the things we like to do. For example, the husband wants to spend his Saturday afternoon watching college football on television, but his wife wants him to catch up on yard work. Or the wife likes the window open in the bedroom at night, while her husband wants it shut.

Sometimes giving a blessing means regarding others as more important than yourself. Read the following passage:

> Do nothing from selfishness or empty conceit, but with humility of mind let each of you regard one another as more important than himself; do not merely look out for your own personal interests, but also for the interests of others. Have this attitude in yourselves which was also in Christ Jesus, who, although He existed in the form of God, did not regard equality with God a thing to be grasped, but emptied Himself, taking the form of a bond-servant, and being made in the likeness of men. And being found in appearance as a man, He humbled Himself by becoming obedient to the point of death, even death on a cross. (Philippians 2:3–8)

What are some examples of how you could give a blessing by doing what your mate wants instead of what you want?

_____

_____

_____

_____

Interact As a Couple:

Share your answers with each other.

E. The Hope of the Holy Spirit

1. Why is giving a blessing after an insult so difficult?

---

2. Read 1 Peter 2:20–24:

> For what credit is there if, when you sin and are harshly treated,
> you endure it with patience? But if when you do what is right and
> suffer for it you patiently endure it, this finds favor with God. For
> you have been called for this purpose, since Christ also suffered
> for you, leaving you an example for you to follow in His steps,
> who committed no sin, nor was any deceit found in His mouth;
> and while being reviled, He did not revile in return; while suffering,
> He uttered no threats, but kept entrusting Himself to Him who
> judges righteously.

a. How did Christ respond to insult?

---

b. What does it mean to entrust yourself "to Him who judges righteously"? Why is this important when working through conflict?

---

c. Can you recall a time when, after an insult, you entrusted your-self to the Father and, in the power of the Holy Spirit, experienced the supernatural ability to respond with a blessing? Share a few of the details.

_____

_____

HomeBuilders Principle #12: As you depend on the Holy Spirit for wisdom and power, you will develop the forgiving and gracious heart you need to respond with a blessing rather than an insult.

F. Conclusion

1. How have the principles you've learned in this entire study helped you begin to resolve conflict in your marriage?

_____

_____

2. What are some principles you feel you need to practice or emphasize more in the future?

_____

_____

Make a Date

Make a date with your mate to meet in the next few days to complete **HomeBuilders Project #6.**

Date	Time	Location

■

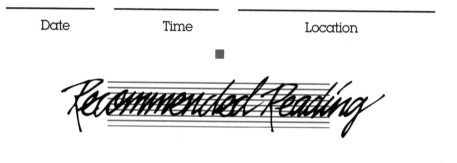

Recommended Reading

Lonely Husbands, Lonely Wives   by Dennis Rainey

■ "Married but lonely" would describe the condition of many people today. Conflicting work schedules, differences in upbringing and expectations, selfishness, unexpected difficulties, and countless other factors conspire to isolate marriage partners from each other. This tendency will continue, says Dennis Rainey, unless the couple has a plan of action to combat these destructive forces and deliberately works to build oneness and intimacy. Here is a master plan for oneness, based squarely on biblical principles, to enable you to build a marriage of strength and lasting intimacy.

Building Your Mate's Self-Esteem by Dennis and Barbara Rainey

■ In this book, Dennis and Barbara Rainey offer you insight into God's selfless, self-giving formula for marriage. This intensely practical book teaches you how to deal with the haunting problems of the past, how to give your mate the freedom to fail, how to help your mate be liberated from self-doubt, and provides other creative ideas to help you achieve immediate results.

The Blessing by Gary Smalley and John Trent

■ *The Blessing* is a common-sense depiction of a tradition that was old in the days of Isaac and Abraham, one that is pivotal to the understanding of a host of biblical truths. Gary Smalley and John Trent detail the five elements of the blessing: (1) meaningful touch, (2) the spoken word, (3) the expression of high value, (4) the description of a special future, and (5) the application of genuine commitment. This book offers solid, practical advice for individuals, families, counselors, and pastors.

Individually: 30 minutes

1. Review the entire **Blueprints** section.

2. People typically react to an insult in one of two ways: withdrawing or attacking.

How would you rate your own tendency toward withdrawing or attacking in response to conflict? (Circle the appropriate number.)

WITHDRAW

1	2	3	4	5	6	7	8	9	10

low   high

ATTACK

1	2	3	4	5	6	7	8	9	10

low   high

3.

How would you rate your mate's tendencies?

WITHDRAW

1	2	3	4	5	6	7	8	9	10

low   high

ATTACK

1	2	3	4	5	6	7	8	9	10

low   high

4.

Use the chart on the following page to become a better student of yourself and your reactions. This exercise will also help you come up with the right responses to insulting remarks.

a.   Consider, "In what areas do I tend to react against my mate?" List the situations in the first column of the chart.

b.   List your typical responses to each situation in the second column.

c.   Rank the magnitude of the problems caused by each situation as (H) high, (M) medium, or (L) low and list your ranking in the third column.

d.   In the fourth column, list how you think you *should* respond in the situation.

a. SITUATION	b. USUAL RESPONSE	c. MAGNITUDE OF PROBLEM	d. BETTER RESPONSE

5. How can you better "seek peace and pursue it" in your marriage relationship?

_____

_____

6. Write down some past examples of how you have reacted to an insult by returning another insult. How could you have returned a blessing in each situation?

_____

_____

Interact As a Couple: 25–30 minutes

1. Share each of your answers from the individual section with each other, and look at each other's charts. If necessary, you may need to practice the principles from Session Five and ask for forgiveness.

2. Talk together about what it means to "entrust" yourself to "the One who judges righteously." How will each of you know when the other is doing that?

_____

_____

3. Pray together, asking the Lord to give you wisdom as you seek a blessing-for-insult relationship. Thank Him for the blessings that you will inherit, according to His promise, as you live according to His design.

Conclusion

Where do you go from here?

Where Do You Go from Here?

As we learned in this study, couples need to know how to resolve conflict if they desire to build a solid marriage. Of the available options, either worldly or biblical, the biblical guidelines God has ordained for us to use are clearly best. Often, the truths which Scripture unveils are simple, basic, and clear. This does not necessarily mean, however, that they are easy to implement on a practical, day-to-day basis.

Building your marriage upon these truths may not be popular today, but it will have powerful results. You have probably already caught some special glimpses of that power through your investment of study, discussion, and application. If the truth within this couples study has at times shaken your marriage, it has done so only to strengthen it. We hope you have experienced a sense of strengthening.

But let's not stop here! If this HomeBuilders Couples Series study has helped you and your marriage, let's go on. And in going on, why not ask other couples to join you? By personally beginning another HomeBuilders study, you will not only add additional mortar to your own marriage; you will help strengthen other marriages as well. As Christians, we are not just trying to improve ourselves . . . we are trying to reach the world! This is our ultimate objective in The HomeBuilders Couples Series. Will you now help us help others?

Will you join us in touching lives and changing families?

The following are some practical ways you can make a difference in families today:

1. Gather a group of couples (four to seven) and lead them through the six sessions of the HomeBuilders study you just completed.

2. Commit to participate in other HomeBuilders studies such as *Building Your Marriage, Strengthening Your Mate's Self-Esteem, Building Teamwork in Marriage,* or *Mastering Your Money in Marriage.*

3. Begin weekly family nights—teaching your children about Christ, the Bible, and the Christian life.

4. Host an Evangelistic Dinner Party—invite your non-Christian friends to your home and as a couple share your faith in Christ and the forgiveness of His Gospel.

5. Share the Good News of Jesus Christ with neighborhood children.

6. If you have attended the Family Life Conference, why not assist your pastor in counseling pre-marrieds using the material you received?

7. Talk to your pastor about renting The HomeBuilders Film Series for your church. This is a six-part series on marriage which is currently available for church showings.

For more information on any of the ministry opportunities listed above, contact your local church, or write:

Family Ministry
P.O. Box 23840
Little Rock, AR 72221–3840
(501) 223-8663

The HomeBuilders

C O U P L E S   S E R I E S

"Unless the Lord builds the house,
they labor in vain who build it."
Psalm 127:1

APPENDIX A

The Four Spiritual Laws*

Just as there are physical laws that govern the physical universe, so are there spiritual laws which govern your relationship with God.

LAW ONE: God loves you and offers a wonderful plan for your life.

God's Love

"For God so loved the world, that He gave His only begotten Son, that whoever believes in Him should not perish, but have eternal life" (John 3:16).

God's Plan

(Christ speaking) "I came that they might have life, and might have it abundantly" (that it might be full and meaningful) (John 10:10).

Why is it that most people are not experiencing the abundant life? Because . . .

LAW TWO: Man is sinful and separated from God. Therefore, he cannot know and experience God's love and plan for his life.

Man Is Sinful

"For all have sinned and fall short of the glory of God" (Romans 3:23).

Man was created to have fellowship with God; but, because of his stubborn self-will, chose to go his own independent way, and fellowship with God was broken. This self-will, characterized by an attitude of active rebellion or passive indifference, is evidence of what the Bible calls sin.

Man Is Separated

"For the wages of sin is death" (spiritual separation from God) (Romans 6:23).

```
            \  HOLY GOD  /

              ↑   ↑   ↑ ↑
            / SINFUL MAN \
```

This diagram illustrates that God is holy and man is sinful. A great gulf separates the two. The arrows illustrate that man is continually trying to reach God and the abundant life through his own efforts, such as a good life, philosophy, or religion.

The third law explains the only way to bridge this gulf . . .

> **LAW THREE: Jesus Christ is God's only provision for man's sin. Through Him you can know and experience God's love and plan for your life.**

He Died in Our Place

"But God demonstrates His own love toward us, in that while we were yet sinners, Christ died for us" (Romans 5:8).

He Rose from the Dead

"Christ died for our sins . . . He was buried . . . He was raised on the third day according to the Scriptures . . . He appeared to

[Peter], then to the twelve. After that He appeared to more than five hundred . . ." (1 Corinthians 15:3–6).

He Is the Only Way to God

"Jesus said to him, 'I am the way, and the truth, and the life; no one comes to the Father, but through Me'" (John 14:6).

This diagram illustrates that God has bridged the gulf which separates us from Him by sending His Son, Jesus Christ, to die on the cross in our place to pay the penalty for our sins.

It is not enough just to know these three laws . . .

> **LAW FOUR: We must individually receive Jesus Christ as Savior and Lord; then we can know and experience God's love and plan for our lives.**

We Must Receive Christ

"But as many as received Him, to them He gave the right to become children of God, even to those who believe in His name" (John 1:12).

We Receive Christ through Faith

"For by grace you have been saved through faith; and that not of yourselves, it is the gift of God; not as a result of works, that no one should boast" (Ephesians 2:8–9).

When We Receive Christ, We Experience a New Birth

(Read John 3:1–8.)

We Receive Christ by Personal Invitation

(Christ is speaking): "Behold, I stand at the door and knock; if any one hears My voice and opens the door, I will come in to him" (Revelation 3:20).

Receiving Christ involves turning to God from self (repentance) and trusting Christ to come into our lives to forgive our sins and to make us the kind of people He wants us to be. Just to agree intellectually that Jesus Christ is the Son of God and that He died on the cross for our sins is not enough. Nor is it enough to have an emotional experience. We receive Jesus Christ by faith, as an act of the will.

These two circles represent two kinds of lives:

SELF-DIRECTED LIFE

S —Self is on the throne
†—Christ is outside the life
•—Interests are directed by self, often resulting in discord and frustration

CHRIST-DIRECTED LIFE

†—Christ is in the life and on the throne
S —Self is yielding to Christ
•—Interests are directed by Christ, resulting in harmony with God's plan

Which circle best represents your life?

Which circle would you like to have represent your life?

You ou Can Receive Christ Right Now by Faith through Prayer

(Prayer is talking with God.)

God knows your heart and is not so concerned with your words as He is with the attitude of your heart. The following is a suggested prayer:

> "Lord Jesus, I need You. Thank You for dying on the cross for my sins. I open the door of my life and receive You as my Savior and Lord. Thank You for forgiving my sins and giving me eternal life. Make me the kind of person You want me to be."

Does this prayer express the desire of your heart?

If it does, pray this prayer right now, and Christ will come into your life, as He promised.

APPENDIX B

Have You Made the Wonderful Discovery of the Spirit-Filled Life?*

Every day can be an exciting adventure for the Christian who knows the reality of being filled with the Holy Spirit and who lives constantly, moment by moment, under His gracious control.

The Bible tells us that there are three kinds of people:

1. NATURAL MAN (one who has not received Christ)

"But a natural man does not accept the things of the Spirit of God; for they are foolishness to him, and he cannot understand them, because they are spiritually appraised" (1 Corinthians 2:14).

SELF-DIRECTED LIFE

S—Ego or finite self is on the throne
†—Christ is outside the life
•—Interests are controlled by self, often resulting in discord and frustration

2. SPIRITUAL MAN (one who is controlled and empowered by the Holy Spirit)

"But he who is spiritual appraises all things . . ." (1 Corinthians 2:15).

CHRIST-DIRECTED LIFE

†—Christ is on the throne of the life
S—Ego or self is dethroned
•—Interests are under control of infinite God, resulting in harmony with God's plan

3. CARNAL MAN (one who has received Christ, but who lives in defeat because he trusts in his own efforts to live the Christian life)

SELF-DIRECTED LIFE

E—Ego or finite self is on the throne
†—Christ is dethroned
• —Interests are controlled by self, often resulting in discord and frustration

"And I, brethren, could not speak to you as to spiritual men, but as to carnal men, as to babes in Christ. I gave you milk to drink, not solid food; for you were not yet able to receive it. Indeed, even now you are not yet able, for you are still carnal. For since there is jealousy and strife among you, are you not fleshly, and are you not walking like mere men?" (1 Corinthians 3:1–3).

A. God has Provided for Us an Abundant and Fruitful Christian Life.

Jesus said, "I came that they might have life, and might have it abundantly" (John 10:10).

"I am the vine, you are the branches; he who abides in Me, and I in him, he bears much fruit; for apart from Me you can do nothing" (John 15:5).

"But the fruit of the Spirit is love, joy, peace, patience, kindness, goodness, faithfulness, gentleness, self-control; against such things there is no law" (Galatians 5:22, 23).

"But you shall receive power when the Holy Spirit has come upon you; and you shall be My witnesses both in Jerusalem, and in all Judea and Samaria, and even to the remotest part of the earth" (Acts 1:8).

THE SPIRITUAL MAN

Some Personal Traits Which Result from Trusting God:

Christ-centered
Empowered by the Holy Spirit
Introduces others to Christ
Effective prayer life
Understands God's Word
Trusts God
Obeys God

Love
Joy
Peace
Patience
Kindness
Goodness
Faithfulness

The degree to which these traits are manifested in the life depends upon the extent to which the Christian trusts the Lord with every detail of his life, and upon his maturity in Christ. One who is only beginning to understand the ministry of the Holy Spirit should not be discouraged if he is not as fruitful as more mature Christians who have known and experienced this truth for a longer period.

Why is it that most Christians are not experiencing the abundant life?

B. Carnal Christians Cannot Experience the Abundant and Fruitful Christian Life.

The carnal man trusts in his own efforts to live the Christian life:

1. He is either uninformed about, or has forgotten, God's love, forgiveness, and power (Romans 5:8–10; Hebrews 10:1–25; 1 John 1; 2:1–3; 2 Peter 1:9; Acts 1:8).

2. He has an up-and-down spiritual experience.

3. He cannot understand himself—he wants to do what is right, but cannot.

4. He fails to draw upon the power of the Holy Spirit to live the Christian life.

(1 Corinthians 3:1–3; Romans 7:15–24; 8:7; Galatians 5:16–18)

THE CARNAL MAN

Some or all of the following traits may characterize the Christian who does not fully trust God:

Ignorance of his
   spiritual heritage
Unbelief
Disobedience
Loss of love for God and
   for others
Poor prayer life
No desire for Bible study

Legalistic attitude
Discouragement
Impure thoughts
Jealousy
Guilt
Critical spirit
Worry
Frustration
Aimlessness

(The individual who professes to be a Christian but who continues to practice sin should realize that he may not be a Christian at all, according to 1 John 2:3; 3:6–9; Ephesians 5:5.)

The third truth gives us the only solution to this problem . . .

C. Jesus Promised the Abundant and Fruitful Life as the Result of Being Filled (Controlled and Empowered) by the Holy Spirit.

The Spirit-filled life is the Christ-controlled life, by which Christ lives His life in and through us in the power of the Holy Spirit (John 15).

1. One becomes a Christian through the ministry of the Holy Spirit, according to John 3:1–8. From the moment of spiritual birth, the Christian is indwelt by the Holy Spirit at all times (John 1:12; Colossians 2:9–10; John 14:16–17). Though all Christians are indwelt by the Holy Spirit, not all Christians are filled (controlled and empowered) by the Holy Spirit.

2. The Holy Spirit is the source of the overflowing life (John 7:37–39).

3. The Holy Spirit came to glorify Christ (John 16:1–5). When one is filled with the Holy Spirit, he is a true disciple of Christ.

4. In His last command before His ascension, Christ promised the power of the Holy Spirit to enable us to be witnesses for Him (Acts 1:1–9).

How, then, can one be filled with the Holy Spirit?

D. **We Are Filled (Controlled and Empowered) by the Holy Spirit by Faith; Then We Can Experience the Abundant and Fruitful Life Which Christ Promised to Each Christian.**

You can appropriate the filling of the Holy Spirit *right now* if you:

1. Sincerely desire to be controlled and empowered by the Holy Spirit (Matthew 5:6; John 7:37–39).

2. Confess your sins.

By faith thank God that He has forgiven all of your sins—past, present, and future—because Christ died for you (Colossians 2:13–15; 1 John 1; 2:1–3; Hebrews 10:1–17).

3. By faith claim the fullness of the Holy Spirit, according to:

a. HIS COMMAND—Be filled with the Spirit. "And do not get drunk with wine, for that is dissipation, but be filled with the Spirit" (Ephesians 5:18).

b. HIS PROMISE—He will always answer when we pray according to His will. "And this is the confidence which we have before Him, that, if we ask anything according to His will, He hears us. And if we know that He hears us in whatever we ask, we know that we have the requests which we have asked from Him" (1 John 5:14–15).

Faith can be expressed through prayer . . .

How to Pray in Faith to Be Filled with the Holy Spirit

We are filled with the Holy Spirit by *faith* alone. However, true prayer is one way of expressing your faith. The following is a suggested prayer:

> *"Dear Father, I need You. I acknowledge that I have been in control of my life; and that, as a result, I have sinned against You. I thank You that You have forgiven my sins through Christ's death on the cross for me. I now invite Christ to again take control of the throne of my life. Fill me with the Holy Spirit as You commanded me to be filled, and as You promised in your Word that You would do if I asked in faith. I pray this in the name of Jesus. As an expression of my faith, I now thank You for taking control of my life and for filling me with the Holy Spirit."*

Does this prayer express the desire of your heart? If so, bow in prayer and trust God to fill you with the Holy Spirit right now.

How to Know that You are Filled (Controlled and Empowered) by the Holy Spirit

Did you ask God to fill you with the Holy Spirit? Do you know that you are now filled with the Holy Spirit? On what authority? (On the trustworthiness of God Himself and His Word: Hebrews 11:6; Romans 14:22–23).

Do not depend upon feelings. The promise of God's Word, not our feelings, is our authority. The Christian lives by faith (trust) in the trustworthiness of God Himself and His Word. This train diagram illustrates the relationship between **fact** (God and His Word), **faith** (our trust in God and His Word), and **feeling** (the result of our faith and obedience) (John 14:21).

The train will run with or without the caboose. However, it would be futile to attempt to pull the train by the caboose. In the same way, we, as Christians, do not depend upon feelings or emotions, but we place our faith (trust) in the trustworthiness of God and the promises of His Word.

How to Walk in the Spirit

Faith (trust in God and His promises) is the only means by which a Christian can live the Spirit-controlled life. As you continue to trust Christ moment by moment:

1. Your life will demonstrate more and more of the fruit of the Spirit (Galatians 5:22–23); and will be more and more conformed to the image of Christ (Romans 12:2; 2 Corinthians 3:18).

2. Your prayer life and study of God's Word will become more meaningful.

3. You will experience His power in witnessing (Acts 1:8).

4. You will be prepared for spiritual conflict against the world (1 John 2:15–17); against the flesh (Galatians 5:16–17); and against Satan (1 Peter 5:7–9; Ephesians 6:10–13).

5. You will experience His power to resist temptation and sin (1 Corinthians 10:13; Philippians 4:13; Ephesians 1:19–23; 6:10; 2 Timothy 1:7; Romans 6;1–16).

Spiritual Breathing

By faith you can continue to experience God's love and forgiveness.

If you become aware of an area of your life (an attitude or an action) that is displeasing to the Lord, even though you are walking with Him and sincerely desiring to serve Him, simply thank God that

He has forgiven your sins—past, present and future—on the basis of Christ's death on the cross. Claim His love and forgiveness by faith and continue to have fellowship with Him.

If you retake the throne of your life through sin—a definite act of disobedience—breathe spiritually.

Spiritual Breathing (exhaling the impure and inhaling the pure) is an exercise in faith that enables you to continue to experience God's love and forgiveness.

1. EXHALE—confess your sin—agree with God concerning your sin and thank Him for His forgiveness of it, according to 1 John 1:9 and Hebrews 10:1–25. Confession involves repentance—a change in attitude and action.

2. INHALE—surrender the control of your life to Christ, and appropriate (receive) the fullness of the Holy Spirit by faith. Trust that He now controls and empowers you, according to the *command* of Ephesians 5:18 and the *promise* of 1 John 5:14–15.

About the Authors:

Bob and Jan Horner have long been co-workers—as partners in marriage, parents of three daughters, staff members of Campus Crusade for Christ International, and speakers at Family Life Conferences.

Bob is a graduate of Westmont College and the University of Colorado in mechanical engineering. He joined the staff of Campus Crusade for Christ International in 1964. Jan became part of Campus Crusade two years later, after finishing her education at Colorado State University.

Together, Bob and Jan have invested over ten years in addressing the needs of couples. Their daughters are Kelley, Shawna, and Andrea—and they all love calling Boulder, Colorado, "home."

More Helps For The Home

Build Your Marriage by Asking the Right Questions.

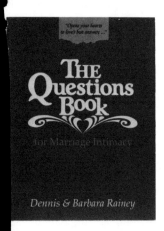

The Questions Book by Dennis and Barbara Rainey gives you 31 questions you've never thought to ask your mate. Thirty-one questions that will ignite your curiosity and rekindle your fascination for each other.

A great marriage takes communication and *The Questions Book* will guide and encourage you and your mate to practice heart-to-heart communication. These questions will spark many memorable hours of sharing, sharpen your understanding of your mate, and stimulate closeness in new areas of your marriage.

The Questions Book...because your marriage is worth it.

Build Your Marriage by Building Your Mate's Self-Esteem.

Unique among human relationships, your marriage has the greatest potential for building your mate's self-esteem. It is also the arena in which the greatest needs for self-esteem become evident.

Moving to meet this essential need head-on are Dennis and Barbara Rainey, authors of the newly released, *Building Your Mate's Self-Esteem*. In their book, the Raineys offer you insight into God's self-less, self-giving formula for marriage. This intensely practical book teaches you how to deal with the haunting problems of the past, how to give your mate the freedom to fail, how to help your mate be liberated from the questions of self-doubt and other creative ideas for immediate results.

Get your copy today, and learn practical, proven ways to build self-esteem through your marriage.

FAMILY MINISTRY